EAT
MY
DUST

JIM DAVIS

ℝ
RAVETTE PUBLISHING

First published by Ravette Publishing 2001

_____

Printed and bound in Great Britain
for Ravette Publishing Limited,
Unit 3, Tristar Centre,
Star Road, Partridge Green,
West Sussex RH13 8RA
by Cox & Wyman Ltd, Reading, Berkshire

ISBN: 1 84161 098 4

GARFIELD!

I DON'T RECALL YOU APPLYING FOR A PERMIT TO BUILD A BAY WINDOW...

JIM DAViS 8-15

"MY OWNER'S A DORK"?

THAT HAD BETTER BE A **TEMPORARY** TATTOO!

HELLO? NO, THIS ISN'T ZONTAR, KING OF THE PIG PEOPLE

STRANGE CALL

NO TIME TO VISIT. I'M HEADED TO MY LODGE MEETING

SOMEBODY CLOSE THAT WINDOW!

JIM DAVIS 10-31

OTHER GARFIELD BOOKS AVAILABLE

Pocket Books	Price	ISBN
Bon Appetit	£3.50	1 84161 038 0
Byte Me	£3.50	1 84161 009 7
Double Trouble	£3.50	1 84161 008 9
A Gift For You	£3.50	1 85304 190 4
The Gladiator	£3.50	1 85304 941 7
Goooooooal!	£3.50	1 84161 037 2
Great Impressions	£3.50	1 85304 191 2
Hangs On	£2.99	1 85304 784 8
Here We Go Again	£2.99	0 948456 10 8
In Training	£3.50	1 85304 785 6
The Irresistible	£3.50	1 85304 940 9
Le Magnifique!	£3.50	1 85304 243 9
Let's Party	£3.50	1 85304 906 9
Light Of My Life	£3.50	1 85304 353 2
On The Right Track	£3.50	1 85304 907 7
Pick Of The Bunch	£2.99	1 85304 258 7
Says It With Flowers	£2.99	1 85304 316 8
Shove At First Sight	£3.50	1 85304 990 5
To Eat Or Not To Eat?	£3.50	1 85304 991 3
Wave Rebel	£3.50	1 85304 317 6
With Love From Me To You	£3.50	1 85304 392 3

new title available Feb 2002:

No. 43 - Fun in the Sun	£3.50	1 84161 097 6

Theme Books		
Guide to Behaving Badly	£4.50	1 85304 892 5
Guide to Being a Couch Potato	£3.99	1 84161 039 9
Guide to Creatures Great & Small	£3.99	1 85304 998 0
Guide to Friends	£3.99	1 84161 040 2
Guide to Healthy Living	£3.99	1 85304 972 7
Guide to Insults	£3.99	1 85304 895 X
Guide to Pigging Out	£4.50	1 85304 893 3
Guide to Romance	£3.99	1 85304 894 1
Guide to The Seasons	£3.99	1 85304 999 9
Guide to Successful Living	£3.99	1 85304 973 5

new titles now available:

Guide to Coffee Mornings	£4.50	1 84161 086 0
Guide to Cat Napping	£4.50	1 84161 087 9

Classics	Price	ISBN
Volume One	£4.99	1 85304 970 0
Volume Two	£5.99	1 85304 971 9
Volume Three	£5.99	1 85304 996 4
Volume Four	£5.99	1 85304 997 2
Volume Five	£4.99	1 84161 022 4
Volume Six	£5.99	1 84161 023 2

new titles now available:

Volume Seven	£5.99	1 84161 088 7
Volume Eight	£5.99	1 84161 089 5

Miscellaneous

new title now available

Garfield Treasury 2	£9.99	1 84161 042 9
Garfield Address Book (indexed)	£4.99 inc VAT	1 85304 904 2
Garfield 21st Birthday Celebration Book	£9.99	1 85304 995 6

All Garfield books are available at your local bookshop or from the address below. Just tick the titles required and send the form with your payment to:-

BBCS, P O Box 941, Kingston upon Hull HU1 3YQ
24-hour telephone credit card line 01482 224626
Prices and availability are subject to change without notice.
Please enclose a cheque or postal order made payable to BBCS to the value of the cover price of the book and allow the following for postage and packing:-

UK & BFPO:	£1.95 (weight up to 1kg)	3-day delivery
	£2.95 (weight over 1kg up to 20kg)	3-day delivery
	£4.95 (weight up to 20kg)	next day delivery

EU & Eire:	Surface Mail	£2.50 for first book & £1.50 for subsequent books
	Airmail	£4.00 for first book & £2.50 for subsequent books
USA:	Surface Mail	£4.50 for first book & £2.50 for subsequent books
	Airmail	£7.50 for first book & £3.50 for subsequent books
Rest of the World:	Surface Mail	£6.00 for first book & £3.50 for subsequent books
	Airmail	£10.00 for first book & £4.50 for subsequent books

Name ....

Address ....

....

....

Cards accepted: Visa, Mastercard, Switch, Delta, American Express

Expiry Date........................Signature ....